~RHYME~
~TIME~

This Little Pig
& OTHER RHYMES

Illustrated by
Kareen Taylorson

MULBERRY EDITIONS

This little pig went to market

This little pig went to market,
This little pig stayed at home,
This little pig had roast beef,
This little pig had none,
And this little pig cried, Wee, wee, wee,
All the way home.

Goosey, goosey gander

Goosey, goosey gander,
Whither shall I wander?
Upstairs and downstairs
And in my lady's chamber.

There I met an old man
Who would not say his prayers.
I took him by the left leg
And threw him down the stairs.

Three blind mice

Three blind mice, see how they run!
They all ran after the farmer's wife,
Who cut off their tails with a carving knife,
Did you ever see such a thing in your life,
As three blind mice?

Here we go round the mulberry bush

Here we go round the mulberry bush,
The mulberry bush, the mulberry bush,
Here we go round the mulberry bush,
On a cold and frosty morning.

This is the way we clap our hands,
Clap our hands, clap our hands,
This is the way we clap our hands,
On a cold and frosty morning.

Six little mice

Six little mice sat down to spin,
Pussy passed by, and she peeped in.
"What are you at, my little men?"
"Making coats for gentlemen."
"Shall I come in and bite off your threads?"
"No, no Miss Pussy, you'll snip off our heads."
"Oh, no, I'll not, I'll help you to spin."
"That may be so, but you don't come in!"

Ding, dong, bell

Ding, dong, bell,
Pussy's in the well.
Who put her in?
Little Johnny Green.

Who pulled her out?
Little Tommy Stout.
What a naughty boy was that
To try and drown poor pussy cat,
Who never did him any harm
And who killed the mice in his father's barn.

The Lion and the Unicorn

The Lion and the Unicorn
Were fighting for the crown;
The Lion beat the Unicorn
All round about the town.
Some gave them white bread,
Some gave them brown;
Some gave them plum cake,
And drummed them out of town.

Two little blackbirds

Two little blackbirds singing in the sun,
One flew away and then there was one;
One little blackbird, very black and tall,
He flew away and then there was the wall.
One little brick wall lonely in the rain,
Waiting for the blackbirds to come and sing again.

I had a little nut tree

I had a little nut tree, nothing would it bear
But a silver nutmeg and a golden pear;
The King of Spain's daughter came to visit me,
And all was because of my little nut tree.
I skipped over water, I danced over sea,
And all the birds in the air couldn't catch me.

Little Bo-peep

Little Bo-peep has lost her sheep,
And doesn't know where to find them;
Leave them alone, and they'll come home,
Bringing their tails behind them.

Hickory, dickory, dock

Hickory, dickory, dock,
The mouse ran up the clock.
The clock struck one,
The mouse ran down,
Hickory, dickory dock.

I love little pussy

I love little pussy, her coat is so warm,
And if I don't hurt her she'll do me no harm,
So I'll not pull her tail, nor drive her away,
But pussy and I very gently will play.

A TEMPLAR BOOK

Devised and produced by Templar Publishing Ltd,
Pippbrook Mill, London Road, Dorking, Surrey RH4 1JE

Copyright © 1987 by Templar Publishing Ltd
Illustrations copyright © 1987 by Templar Publishing Ltd

This 1992 edition produced by
The Templar Company plc for Mulberry Editions,
Great Britain

Printed in Italy